Discover &

Romans in Britain

Activity Book

History Years 3-4

Contents

Published by CGP

Written by Joanna Copley

Editors: Mary Falkner, Rachel Kordan, Sophie Scott, Camilla Simson

Reviewer: Maxine Petrie

ISBN: 978 1 78294 198 9

With thanks to Katherine Faudemer for the proofreading.

With thanks to Laura Jakubowski for the copyright research.

Clipart from Corel®

Discover & Learn

Romans in Britain

Years 3-4

This Activity Book is full of sources and questions to help pupils in Years 3 and 4 explore the KS2 History topic 'The Roman Empire and its Impact on Britain'.

The Romans Invade Britain

Towards the end of the Iron Age, <u>Rome</u> was very <u>different</u> to <u>Britain</u>. Read page 2 of your Study Book to remind you what life was like in Rome and in Britain at this time.

What would it be like living in Rome and Britain towards the end of the Iron Age? Complete the table below to show <u>what life was like</u> in <u>each place</u>.

	Rome	Britain
Who would you be ruled by?		
Would you have to pay taxes?		
Would you have an army to defend you?		

Write down <u>two other differences</u> that there were between Rome and Britain at this time.

1) ....

....

2) ....

....

In 55 BC, <u>Julius Caesar</u> and his army travelled across the <u>English Channel</u> in ships. Have a look at page 3 of your Study Book.

Draw a picture of Caesar and his army <u>arriving in Britain</u>.
Think about <u>where</u> they had to anchor their ships and <u>how</u> they got to shore.

Use page 3 of the Study Book to find out if these sentences about Caesar's first invasion of Britain are <u>true</u> or <u>false</u>. Tick the correct box for each statement.

	True	False
Caesar was prepared for the tides and storms in the English Channel.	☐	☐
Caesar's ships were very big and heavy.	☐	☐
Caesar succeeded in taking over Britain in 55 BC.	☐	☐
Caesar didn't win any battles.	☐	☐
Caesar planned to return to Britain the next year.	☐	☐

"I understand how Britain and Rome were different and I know about Caesar's first invasion of Britain."

Trading and Invading

Archaeologists have found <u>evidence</u> that the people in Britain <u>traded</u> with <u>different</u> <u>countries</u> in Europe <u>before</u> Julius Caesar invaded in 55 BC.

Read page 4 of the Study Book to find out about trading at <u>Hengistbury Head</u>.

Imagine you were <u>trading</u> with the Romans at Hengistbury Head. What might you have <u>bought</u> from the Romans? What might you have <u>given</u> them in return?

From the Romans, I might have bought ....

....

....

In return, I might have given them ....

....

....

By 80 BC, the Celtic tribes in Britain had started to make <u>coins</u>.

Name <u>one thing</u> that people in Britain used for money <u>before</u> they had coins.

....

Imagine you are the <u>leader</u> of a <u>Celtic tribe</u>.
In the box below, <u>design</u> a coin for your tribe to use.

Make sure you design <u>both sides</u> of your coin.

The Romans and the Celtic tribes in Britain had very <u>different</u> ways of <u>fighting</u>.
The picture below shows a <u>chariot</u>. Chariots were used by the Celtic tribes.

Look at the picture and use page 5 of the Study Book
to help you <u>describe</u> how the <u>Celtic tribes</u> fought.

The Celtic tribes in Britain fought by

....

....

....

....

....

Why do you think the <u>Romans won</u> the battles against the tribes?
Write down <u>two reasons</u>

1) ....

2) ....

When did Julius Caesar <u>leave</u> Britain? Why didn't he stay? Use page 5 of the
Study Book and the key words in the box to help you write your answer.

Key Words

Gaul   *rebelling*   summer

Caesar left Britain ....

because ....

....

"I know about trade in Britain before Caesar invaded,
and I know about Caesar's second invasion of Britain."

Britain Between the Caesars

Julius Caesar was killed in 44 BC. The three Roman emperors who came after him didn't invade Britain.

> Imagine you were the emperor of Rome. Would you have tried to invade Britain? Explain your answer.

I .... have tried to invade Britain because

....

....

....

At this time in Britain, new settlements were forming. These were called oppida.

> Use page 6 of the Study Book to find out if these sentences about life in oppida are true or false. Tick the correct box for each statement.

	True	False
Oppida were very small settlements.	☐	☐
The houses in an oppidum were arranged along streets.	☐	☐
You could live and work in an oppidum.	☐	☐
You might find people working with metal in an oppidum.	☐	☐

Read about Roman glass on page 7 of your Study Book.

> In your own words, explain why owning glass meant that you were rich and powerful.

....

....

Imagine you are walking through an oppidum. What do you think you would <u>see</u>, <u>hear</u> and <u>smell</u>? Write your ideas in the box.

We know that people living in Britain around this time used <u>olive oil</u> and <u>wine</u> that came from the Roman Empire.

Can you think of any <u>foods</u> that <u>you</u> eat that don't come from Britain? Do you know where they come from?

In your own words, explain why the people in Britain <u>couldn't</u> make their own <u>wine</u>.

"I know what an oppidum is and I know how the Romans started to influence the lives of people living in Britain."

Calleva Atrebatum

Calleva Atrebatum was an oppidum.
Read about Calleva on page 8 of your Study Book.

Are these sentences about Calleva Atrebatum true or false?
Tick the correct box for each statement.

	True	False
Calleva Atrebatum is now called Colchester.	☐	☐
Calleva Atrebatum was an unplanned jumble of houses.	☐	☐
Calleva Atrebatum was built on a grid like a Roman town.	☐	☐

Use page 8 of your Study Book and what you know
about oppida to answer the questions below.

You can read about oppida on pages 6 and 7 of your Study Book.

Lots of people visited big settlements like Calleva.
What do you think they came to Calleva for?

I think people visited Calleva to ....

....

Look at the picture of Calleva on page 8 of the Study Book. Write down some
of the things that you think the buildings in the picture would have been used for.

I think the buildings would have been used for ....

....

Why do archaeologists think that people in Calleva Atrebatum worked gold?

Archaeologists think that people worked gold in Calleva because ....

....

Look at page 9 of your Study Book. Read about what happened to <u>Commius</u>. Imagine it is 53 BC and you are Commius. You've just found out that one of <u>Caesar's army chiefs</u> wants to <u>meet</u> with you.

In the box below, write a <u>diary entry</u> for that day. Include what happened when you met the army chief, how you felt about it and what you plan to do next. Use the information on page 9 of your Study Book to help you.

Read about the <u>kings of Calleva</u> on page 9 of your Study Book.

Why was it a <u>mistake</u> for <u>Verica</u> to ask Rome for help?

....

....

"I know about the history of Calleva Atrebatum, and I know what life was like for the people who lived there."

Claudius the Conqueror

When <u>Claudius</u> became the Roman emperor he decided to <u>invade Britain</u>.
Read page 10 of your Study Book.

Why did Claudius decide to <u>invade</u> Britain?

....

....

Are these sentences about Claudius <u>true</u> or <u>false</u>?
Tick the correct box for each statement.

	True	False
Claudius was never ill.	☐	☐
Claudius was Gaius Caligula's father.	☐	☐
Claudius had a stammer.	☐	☐

When <u>Claudius</u> invaded Britain, he was <u>well prepared</u> for battle.
Read page 10 of your Study Book.

In the box below, draw a picture of a <u>battle</u>
between the Celtic tribes and the Roman army.

Have a look back at page 5 of your Study Book if you need a reminder of how the Celtic tribes fought.

The picture below shows a Roman <u>war elephant</u>.

Imagine you are a member of a Celtic tribe in a <u>battle</u> against the Roman army.

How do you think you'd have <u>felt</u> when you
first saw the <u>Roman army</u>? Explain your answer.

I'd have felt ....

because ....

....

....

....

<u>Eleven</u> of the tribes from the south east of Britain <u>surrendered</u> to the Romans.
Read page 11 of your Study Book.

Do you think <u>you</u> would have surrendered to the Romans? Why or why not?

I .... *have surrendered to the Romans because*

....

....

Read about <u>client kings</u> on page 11 of your Study Book.

Circle the <u>correct word or words</u> from each pair
to complete these sentences about <u>client kings</u>.

*Client kings were (<u>allies</u> / <u>enemies</u>) of Rome. They (<u>paid</u> / <u>didn't pay</u>)
taxes. They were expected to leave their land to (<u>Rome</u> / <u>their children</u>).*

"I understand why Claudius invaded Britain and
I know what happened during the invasion."

The Roman Army

Rome's <u>army</u> was the reason it managed to <u>conquer</u> so many other countries.
Read about the different <u>types of soldier</u> on pages 12 and 13 of your Study Book.

In the box, draw a picture of a <u>standard bearer</u>.
Describe the job he did in the Roman army.

I am a standard bearer in the Roman army.

My job is to ....

....

....

....

....

....

Name <u>three</u> other jobs that you could do in the Roman army.

1) ....

2) ....

3) ....

One of the reasons the Roman army was so successful was that it was <u>well organised</u>.

Have a look at page 13 of your Study Book. Fill in the gaps in these sentences.

Soldiers in the Roman army were divided into groups of .... *men*

called centuries. Each century was led by a ....

Centuries joined to form groups of .... *men called legions.*

These were led by a ....

Read about <u>joining</u> the Roman army on page 12 of your Study Book.

In this box, write the <u>good things</u> and the <u>bad things</u> about <u>joining</u> the Roman army.

Good things about joining the Roman army:	Bad things about joining the Roman army:

Would <u>you</u> have joined the Roman army if you were a young man?
Explain your answer.

I .... *have joined the Roman army because*

....

The Romans let men from countries they'd conquered join their army.
Read about this on page 13 of your Study Book.

Give <u>two</u> ways that this helped the Roman army.

1) ....

....

2) ....

....

"I know about the Roman army and
why it was important to Rome's success."

Building Roads to Conquer

The Romans built lots of <u>roads</u> during their invasion of the <u>south of England</u>. Read pages 14 and 15 of your Study Book.

In your own words, explain why the Romans needed to build roads in Britain. You might want to use the <u>key words</u> in the box to help you write your answer.

Key Words

march   proper roads   dirt tracks   far   quickly

....

....

....

....

The picture below is of a carving which shows some people <u>building a Roman road</u>.

What job do you think the man on the <u>left</u> of the picture is doing?

I think that the man on the left

of the picture is ....

....

....

....

The two men on the <u>right</u> of the picture are hammering a layer of stones down, to make the surface of the road <u>flat</u>.

Do you think it is easier to make flat road surfaces today? Explain your answer.

I think it .... *easier to make flat road surfaces today because*

....

Look at the pictures below.

One picture shows a road built in <u>Roman times</u> and one shows a road from <u>today</u>.

Which do you think is the Roman road? Why?

I think .... *is the Roman road because* ....

....

Give <u>two</u> ways that Roman roads were different from the roads we make today.

1) ....

2) ....

Read pages 14 and 15 of your Study Book.

Are these sentences about Roman roads <u>true</u> or <u>false</u>?
Tick the correct box for each statement.

	True	False
The Romans sometimes used slaves to help build roads.	☐	☐
The Roman roads linked up army forts and towns.	☐	☐
The new roads helped the Roman army to conquer the south of England from west to east.	☐	☐
There would be a mansio roughly every 4 miles along a Roman road.	☐	☐

"I understand why the Romans built roads in Britain."

The Invasion Continues...

The Roman army travelled to <u>Anglesey</u> in <u>Wales</u> to fight the <u>Druids</u>.
Read about the Druids on pages 16 and 17 of your Study Book.

Imagine that you are the <u>leader</u> of the Roman army in Britain. The emperor
has written to you. He wants to know <u>who</u> the Druids are and <u>why</u> you want
to fight them.

Write a <u>letter replying to the emperor</u>.
Explain who the Druids are and why the Romans need to defeat them.

Dear Emperor Nero,

You wanted to know who the Druids are and why it is important

that we defeat them. Well, the Druids are ....

....

....

....

....

....

....

....

....

....

....

Best wishes,
The leader of the Roman army in Britain.

Read page 17 of your Study Book. Imagine you are a soldier in the Roman army and you have just arrived on the beach at <u>Anglesey</u>.

In the box, write or draw what you would have seen. At the bottom of the box, write <u>two</u> words describing how you would have felt.

> *I'd have felt* .... *and* ....

The Romans also went to Wales because they wanted the <u>gold</u> in the Welsh hills. Read page 17 of your Study Book.

Draw a picture showing <u>how</u> the Romans got gold from the Welsh hills. Include as much <u>detail</u> as you can and make sure you <u>label</u> your picture.

"I know why the Romans went to Wales and I understand why they wanted to defeat the Druids."

Turning Britain into Rome

The Romans living in Britain sometimes put on <u>gladiatorial games</u> for entertainment. Gladiators were <u>celebrities</u>. Some of them were paid lots of <u>money</u>, and they had lots of <u>fans</u>, but they risked <u>injury</u> and <u>death</u> every time they went into a fight.

Would you have liked to be a gladiator? Explain why or why not.

I .... *have liked to be a gladiator because* ....

....

....

....

Read pages 18 and 19 of your Study Book.

What type of <u>building</u> were these gladiator combats held in?

....

Name another <u>type of building</u> that was built in Britain by the Romans.

....

The Romans who came to Britain had other types of <u>entertainment</u> too.

Look at the picture on the right. What do you think the picture shows?

....

....

....

19

The Romans liked to make the settlements in Britain more like <u>Rome</u>.
Read pages 18 and 19 of your Study Book.

How do you think the people living in Britain <u>felt</u> about the Romans coming and turning their settlements into '<u>mini-Romes</u>'? Explain your answer.

....

....

....

Use page 19 of the Study Book to find out if these sentences about cities in Britain are <u>true</u> or <u>false</u>. Tick the correct box for each statement.

	True	False
Caerleon was the capital city of Britain in Roman times.	☐	☐
There was an amphitheatre in Caerleon.	☐	☐
The Romans built Londinium in 12 BC.	☐	☐

Look at page 19 of your Study Book.

Why was a temple built to the emperor <u>Claudius</u> in <u>Colchester</u>?

....

....

If the name of a place today ends in '<u>chester</u>', '<u>cester</u>' or '<u>caster</u>' it means that there might have been a Roman site there.

Apart from Colchester, can you think of a place in Britain where there might have been a Roman site?

I think that there was a Roman site at ....

Boudica Bites Back

In AD 60, <u>Prasutagus</u>, king of the Iceni tribe, died.
Read about Prasutagus on page 20 of your Study Book.

<u>Who</u> did Prasutagus <u>leave his kingdom to</u> when he died?

He left some of his kingdom to ....

and some of it to ....

Why wasn't the <u>Roman emperor</u> happy about this?

The Roman emperor wasn't happy about this because ....

....

....

In your own words, explain what the Romans did to <u>Boudica</u> and her tribe.
You might want to use some of the key words in the box below to help you.

Key Words
money   beat   crops   Iceni lands   daughters

....

....

....

....

....

Boudica led the Celtic tribes in a <u>rebellion</u> against the Romans.
Read about Boudica and the tribes on page 21 of your Study Book.

Put these <u>events</u> from the story of Boudica into the <u>right order</u> by numbering the boxes from 1 to 5. The first one has been done for you.

The tribes went on to burn down London. ☐

Boudica led the tribes into a rebellion against the Romans. ☐ 1

The Roman army, though outnumbered, defeated the tribes. ☐

The tribes attacked Colchester, and set fire to the temple. ☐

The Romans marched from Wales to stop the tribes. ☐

A <u>Roman writer</u> called <u>Tacitus</u> wrote about the battle between the Romans and the tribes. He wrote that about <u>80 000</u> people from the tribes died in the battle but only <u>400</u> Romans died.
Some people think this <u>might not be true</u>.

Do you think that what Tacitus wrote is true? Tick the sentence below that you <u>agree</u> with. Explain <u>why</u> you agree with it.

I think Tacitus was telling the truth. ☐

I think Tacitus might have lied. ☐

I think this because ....

....

....

....

....

"I understand why Boudica led the Celtic tribes in rebellion against the Romans."

Towards Scotland

The Romans built lots of <u>forts</u> in Britain to help them <u>stay in control</u> of the tribes. Read about forts on pages 22 and 23 of your Study Book.

Imagine your <u>school</u> is going to be <u>turned into a fort</u>. What would you need to add to your school to help <u>defend it</u>? In the box below, draw your school as it would look if it was a fort. Make sure you <u>label</u> your picture.

Read page 23 of your Study Book. The tribes in Scotland nearly beat the Roman army by launching surprise attacks on them and never meeting them in full battle.

Why did the tribes in Scotland want to <u>avoid</u> meeting the Roman army in a <u>battle</u>?

The tribes in Scotland wanted to avoid having a battle with the Roman

army because ....

....

Read page 23 of your Study Book and look at the picture.

In your own words, explain <u>why</u> the Romans built <u>Hadrian's wall</u>.
You might want to use some of the key words in the box below.

Key Words

withdrawn   emperor Hadrian   separate   attacking   tribes

....

....

....

....

....

Imagine you are a member of one of the <u>tribes</u> from <u>Scotland</u>.

How would you feel about the Romans building Hadrian's wall? Why?

I would feel ....

because ....

....

Now imagine you are a <u>Roman</u> who lives in <u>England</u> just south of Hadrian's wall.

How would you feel about the Romans building Hadrian's wall? Why?

I would feel ....

because ....

....

"I understand why the Romans built forts
and why they built Hadrian's wall."

Building Hadrian's Wall

The Romans built <u>Hadrian's wall</u> to stop the tribes from Scotland invading their lands. Thousands of Roman soldiers lived on the wall, protecting the border.

Use pages 24 and 25 of the Study Book to find out if these sentences about Hadrian's wall are <u>true</u> or <u>false</u>. Tick the correct box for each statement.

	True	False
Hadrian's wall was mostly built from stone.	☐	☐
It took the Romans about a year to build the wall.	☐	☐
There was a big ditch to the north of the wall.	☐	☐
The wall was about 3 metres wide.	☐	☐
There were 16 forts built into the wall.	☐	☐
Each fort was home to about 6000 soldiers.	☐	☐

Imagine you were in <u>charge</u> of <u>keeping</u> the tribes from Scotland <u>out</u> of the Roman land. Draw a diagram to show what <u>defences</u> you would build. Make sure that you <u>label</u> your diagram.

The photo on the right shows the <u>remains</u> of a building on <u>Hadrian's wall</u>. Buildings like this one were found roughly <u>every mile</u> along the wall. Read page 25 of your Study Book.

What <u>type of building</u> do you think these are the remains of?

....

How <u>many</u> soldiers lived in this type of building? Circle your answer.

2 to 3   *20 to 30*   *200 to 300*

The <u>turrets</u> along Hadrian's wall gave the Roman soldiers a <u>good view</u> of the land on <u>both sides</u> of the wall. Look at the picture of a turret on page 25 of the Study Book.

Imagine that you are the soldier standing on the top of the turret. Fill in the table to show what you might see on the <u>north side</u> of the wall and what you might see on the <u>south side</u> of the wall.

Use the diagram of the wall on page 24 of the Study Book to help you imagine what you'd see.

View on the north side	View on the south side

"I know what Hadrian's wall was like and I know that lots of soldiers lived along the wall."

Life at the Edge of the Empire

A large collection of Roman <u>letters</u> was found at one of the forts near Hadrian's wall. They tell us a lot about what life was like for the people who lived on the wall.

Read the information about the letters on page 26 of the Study Book.

> What did the Romans living near Hadrian's wall use to write their letters?

They wrote on ....

They wrote with ....

Think about the last <u>letter</u> or <u>card</u> that you sent or received.

> If someone found this letter or card in 2000 years' time, what would they be able to tell about your life? Write your ideas in the box below.

The letters found near Hadrian's wall tell us what sort of <u>food</u> the Roman soldiers <u>ate</u>. Read page 27 of the Study Book.

> Write down <u>three</u> things that soldiers living in the wall forts ate.

1) ....

2) ....

3) ....

Read page 27 of your Study Book. We know a lot more about what life was like in Britain <u>after</u> the Romans invaded than before they invaded.

Explain why this is. You may want to use some of the <u>key words</u> in the box below.

Key Words

evidence   wrote   archaeologists   information

We know more about what life was like in Britain after the Romans invaded because ....

....

....

Imagine that you are a Roman soldier working at Hadrian's wall. Write a <u>letter</u> to your family back home in Italy telling them what it is like to <u>live on Hadrian's wall</u>.

Try and use everything you've learnt about life at Hadrian's wall on pages 26 and 27 of the Study Book.

"I understand what life was like for the Roman soldiers living on or near Hadrian's wall."

The Roman North

About twenty years after building Hadrian's wall, the Romans built the <u>Antonine wall</u>.

On the map below, draw <u>Hadrian's wall</u> and the <u>Antonine wall</u>.
Label your drawing to show which wall is which.

You can use the map at the back of the Study Book to help you with this question.

Read page 28 of the Study Book.

Circle the correct word or words from each pair to complete these sentences about the Antonine wall.

The Antonine wall was built (north / south) of Hadrian's wall.

The Antonine wall was (15 miles / 80 miles) away from Hadrian's wall.

In your own words, explain <u>why</u> the Romans built the Antonine wall.

....

....

....

In Roman times, the city of <u>York</u> became an <u>army centre</u>.
The Romans built a large <u>fort</u> there. Read page 29 of the Study Book.

Imagine you are a <u>skilled metal worker</u> living in a small village near York.
Would you be pleased that the Romans had built a large fort at York?
Explain your answer.

I .... *be pleased, because* ....

....

....

The picture below shows a part of the York city <u>wall</u>. The <u>lower section</u> of the wall
shows some of the remains of a wall <u>built by the Romans</u>.

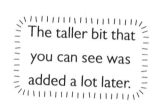
The taller bit that you can see was added a lot later.

<u>Why</u> do you think the Romans <u>built a wall</u> around the city of York?

....

....

....

"I understand why the Romans built the Antonine wall.
I know that York was an important city in Roman times."

Living Like a Roman

Roman men and women <u>weren't equal</u>. They lived quite <u>different lives</u>.
Read page 30 of the Study Book.

For each of the sentences below, decide whether the person speaking is a
Roman <u>man</u> or a Roman <u>woman</u>. If the speaker is a <u>man</u>, colour the speech
bubble in <u>blue</u>. If the speaker is a <u>woman</u> colour the speech bubble in <u>red</u>.

> I am a member of the government.

> I make clothes for my family.

> I have to look after the children.

> I am a soldier in the army.

> I am the emperor of Rome.

> I make sure my household is run properly.

While poor children would have to work, <u>rich</u> Roman children were <u>educated</u>.
Below is a diary entry showing what a day might have been like for a rich Roman child.

> I wake up at sunrise, ready for school. My parents are wealthy so I have a
> tutor who teaches me maths, history and literature. I get a break at lunch,
> but I go back to my studies in the afternoon. When school finishes, there is
> some time to play with my toys before I eat with my mother and go to bed.

Give <u>one</u> way in which your day is <u>different</u> to the day
described above, and then <u>one</u> way in which it is <u>similar</u>.

One way that my day is different is ....

....

One way that my day is similar is ....

....

Life was very different for children from the <u>tribes</u> in Britain.

Name <u>two</u> things that rich children from the tribes would have been taught.

1) ....

2) ....

The Romans built <u>public baths</u> all over Britain.
The picture below shows what we think the public baths might have been like.
Look at the picture and read page 31 of your Study Book.

Apart from getting washed, <u>why else</u> did the Romans <u>visit</u> the <u>public baths</u>?

....

....

<u>Describe</u> how we think the <u>people in the tribes</u> might have washed.

....

....

....

Archaeologists <u>haven't found</u> any <u>evidence</u> of the tribes in Britain having public baths.

What does this tell us? Tick the statement below that you agree with.

The people in the tribes never washed. ☐

The people in the tribes definitely didn't have public baths. ☐

The people in the tribes probably didn't have public baths. ☐

"I know some of the differences between how people in the tribes lived and how the Romans lived."

Living in Luxury Villas

When the Romans invaded Britain, they brought the art of building <u>villas</u> with them.

Read page 32 of the Study Book. In your own words, explain what a <u>villa</u> was. You might want to use some of the <u>key words</u> from the box below.

Key Words

| Roman | wealthy | mansion | country |

A villa was ....

....

....

The <u>tribes</u> who lived in Britain before the Romans invaded lived in <u>small huts</u>.

What do you think the people in the tribes would have thought of the Roman villas? Explain your answer.

The tribes might have thought that villas were ....

because ....

....

<u>Villas</u> were often made up of lots of <u>buildings</u> and surrounded by lots of <u>land</u>.

Circle the features below that you think a <u>Roman villa</u> would have had.

cinema room   courtyard   bedroom

bath house   garage

jacuzzi   barn   computer room

storehouse   gardens

The insides of villas were often decorated with <u>mosaics</u>.

In the box below, design a mosaic that could go on the floor inside a Roman villa.

Mosaics would often show scenes from everyday life, events from the past, or things that were important to the Romans — such as gods.

Read page 33 of the Study Book.

Would the <u>floors</u> in a Roman villa have been <u>warm</u> or <u>cold</u>? Tick the correct answer below and explain your choice.

The floors in Roman villas would have been   warm ☐   cold ☐

because ....

....

....

Name <u>two</u> jobs that a <u>slave</u> in a Roman villa might have to do.

1) ....

2) ....

"I know what Roman villas were and I know some of the features that made them luxurious."

Religion in Roman Britain

The Romans worshipped lots of <u>different gods</u>.
This picture shows a statue of one of the Roman gods
called <u>Mars</u>.

Look at the picture of the statue of Mars. What do
you think he was the god of? Explain your answer.

I think Mars was the god of ....

because ....

....

The soldiers at Hadrian's wall worshipped <u>Mithras</u>, the Roman <u>god of soldiers</u>.

Look at the lists below. Draw lines to match the different <u>groups of people</u> on
the left with a <u>god</u> or <u>goddess</u> on the right that might be <u>important</u> to them.

Blacksmiths   Ceres, goddess of crops

Sailors   Mercury, god of trade

Farmers   Neptune, god of the sea

Merchants   Vulcan, god of fire

Read page 35 of the Study Book.
There is some <u>evidence</u> of <u>Christianity</u> in Britain <u>before AD 313</u>.

These early Christians had to meet in <u>secret</u>. Why was this?

Early Christians in Britain had to meet in secret because ....

....

....

Christianity and the Romans' religion were very different.

> Write down one way that the Romans' religion was different to Christianity.

....

....

Eventually, Christianity was made legal by the Roman emperor Constantine.

> Read the statements below and decide whether each
> one is true or false. Tick the correct box for each one.

	True	False
Constantine dreamt that Sulis Minerva spoke to him.	☐	☐
Constantine became Christian after winning a battle.	☐	☐
Christianity was legal in Britain after AD 213.	☐	☐

Archaeologists have found evidence that shows that there were
some Christians in Britain after Christianity became legal.

> Draw one piece of archaeological evidence that shows that there were Christians
> in Britain after Christianity became legal. Describe what you have drawn.

I have drawn ....

"I know about religion in Roman Britain."

Trouble in the Empire

Over the years, the Roman Empire had grown to be very large.
Read pages 36 and 37 of your Study Book.

Why did the size of the Roman Empire begin to cause problems for the Romans?

The size of the Roman Empire began to cause problems because ....

....

....

....

Many Roman soldiers were becoming fed up.

Imagine you're a Roman soldier.
Fill in the speech bubble below to explain why you're fed up.

I'm fed up because ....

....

....

The Romans in Britain were under attack from different tribes from Europe and Britain.
They began to build forts to defend against the Saxons, a tribe from Europe.

On the map below, mark with a cross three places where you would build a fort
to defend against the Saxons. Then, explain why you have chosen these locations.

I would build my forts in these

locations because ....

....

....

....

Read page 37 of the Study Book then read the following
facts about the <u>Roman walls</u> that once stood in <u>London</u>.

> Height – around 6 metres   Width – 2 to 3 metres
> Length – 2 miles   Built from – stone

Do you think the walls in London would have
been good at <u>keeping out raiders</u>? Explain why.

I think the walls in London .... *have been good at*

keeping out raiders because ....

....

....

Archaeologists have found <u>hoards</u> of Roman <u>coins</u> buried around Britain.

Why do you think some people in Britain <u>buried</u> their coins?

I think some people buried their coins because ....

....

Imagine Britain is being invaded <u>today</u>.
In the box below, draw or write down some things that you would bury.

> "I know why Britain began to be attacked and I know
> how the Romans in Britain reacted to these attacks."

The Romans Retreat

The <u>Barbarian Conspiracy</u> happened in the winter of <u>AD 367</u>.
Read page 38 of the Study Book.

Tick the statement below that best describes
what happened during the <u>Barbarian Conspiracy</u>.

The raiding tribes attacked at the same time. ☐

The raiding tribes attacked at different times. ☐

The raiding tribes attacked each other. ☐

The map below shows <u>where</u> the <u>tribes</u> attacked from in the Barbarian Conspiracy.

Fill in the <u>labels</u> on the map to show the <u>direction</u> each tribe attacked from.
Use the <u>names</u> of the tribes from the box on the right.

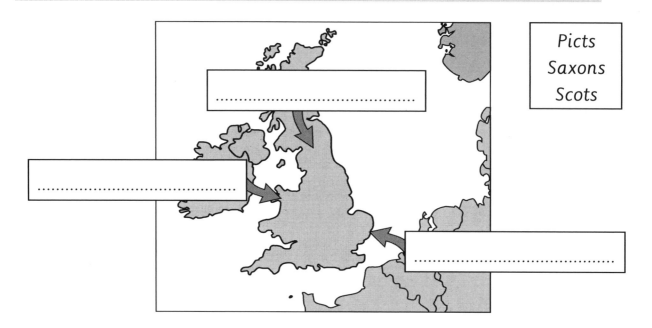

Picts
Saxons
Scots

How do you think you would have felt if you had lived in Britain at this time?
Explain your answer.

I would have felt ....

because ....

....

After the Barbarian Conspiracy, many <u>slaves escaped</u>, formed <u>groups</u> and started <u>destroying Roman buildings</u> in Britain. Read page 39 of the Study Book.

Look at the picture of the <u>villa</u> on page 32 of the Study Book. In the box below, draw what the villa might have looked like after the Barbarian Conspiracy.

The Roman army began to <u>retreat</u> from Britain.

Around when did the Roman army <u>leave Hadrian's wall</u>? Circle the correct answer.

AD 50   AD 100   AD 313   AD 400   200 BC

By AD 410, the Roman army had <u>left Britain</u> altogether.

Do you think this was the <u>right</u> thing or the <u>wrong</u> thing for the Romans to have done? Explain your answer.

I think this was the .... *thing for the Romans to*

have done because ....

....

....

"I know about the Barbarian Conspiracy and how it led to the Romans leaving Britain."

Picture acknowledgements

Cover photo English Heritage / Mary Evans

Thumb illustration used throughout the book © iStockphoto.com

p5 (chariot) © Look and Learn.

p11 (war elephant) Sheila Terry / Science Photo Library.

p14 (Road building) Museo della Civilta Romana, Rome, Italy / Bridgeman Images.

p15 (Roman road) © The Art Archive / Alamy.

p18 (chariot race) © Look and Learn.

p25 (milecastle) © David Robertson / Alamy.

p29 (York city wall) © Peter Brown / Alamy.

p31 (Roman baths) Mary Evans Picture Library.

p34 (Mars) © The Art Archive / Alamy.

Discover & Learn

The Complete Range

Geography

Geography — Years 3-4

Geography — Years 5-6

History

History Years 3-4 — Stone Age to Celts

History Years 3-4 — Romans in Britain

History Years 5-6 — Anglo-Saxons

History Years 5-6 — Vikings

Find out more at cgpbooks.co.uk

Printed in Great Britain
by Amazon